GREEN ARROW

ROAD TO JERICHO

Judd Winick
Writer

Scott McDaniel
Penciller

Andy Owens
Inker

Guy Major
Colorist

Pat Brosseau
Letterer

Scott McDaniel
and Andy Owens
Original Series Covers

DAN DIDIO
Senior VP-Executive Editor
MIKE CARLIN
Editor-original series
TOM PALMER, JR.
Associate Editor-original series
BOB HARRAS
Editor-collected edition
ROBBIN BROSTERMAN
Senior Art Director
PAUL LEVITZ
President & Publisher
GEORG BREWER
VP-Design & DC Direct Creative
RICHARD BRUNING
Senior VP-Creative Director
PATRICK CALDON
Executive VP-Finance & Operations
CHRIS CARAMALIS
VP-Finance
JOHN CUNNINGHAM
VP-Marketing
TERRI CUNNINGHAM
VP-Managing Editor

ALISON GILL
VP-Manufacturing
HANK KANALZ
VP-General Manager, WildStorm
JIM LEE
Editorial Director-WildStorm
PAULA LOWITT
Senior VP-Business & Legal Affairs
MARYELLEN MCLAUGHLIN
VP-Advertising & Custom Publishing
JOHN NEE
VP-Business Development
GREGORY NOVECK
Senior VP-Creative Affairs
SUE POHJA
VP-Book Trade Sales
CHERYL RUBIN
Senior VP-Brand Management
JEFF TROJAN
VP-Business Development, DC Direct
BOB WAYNE
VP-Sales

Cover illustration by Scott McDaniel and Andy Owens.
Cover color by Guy Major.

GREEN ARROW:
ROAD TO JERICHO

DC Comics does not read or accept unsolicited submissions of ideas, stories or artwork.

DC Comics, 1700 Broadway, New York, NY 10019
A Warner Bros. Entertainment Company
Printed in Canada. First Printing.

ISBN: 1-4012-1508-4
ISBN 13: 978-1-4012-1508-8

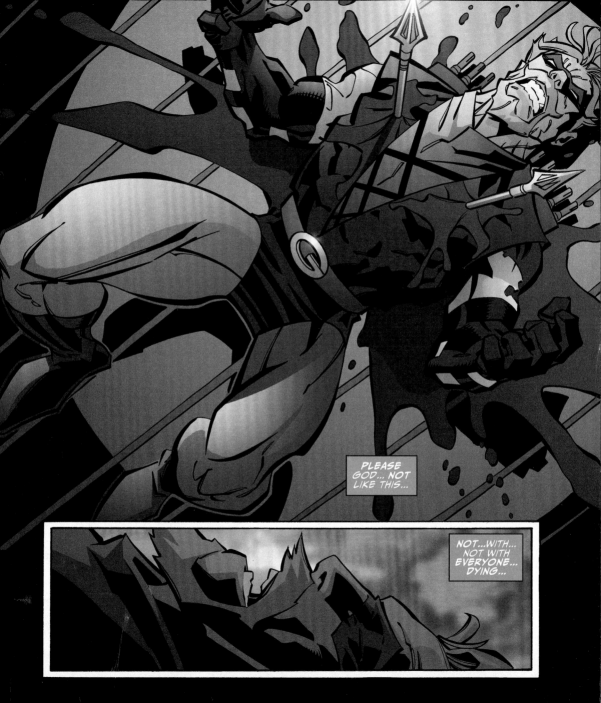

I DON'T KNOW WHO THE HELL THESE BASTARDS THOUGHT THEY WERE DEALING WITH.

BUT IF YOU WERE GOING TO TRY TO TAKE ME DOWN--

--YOU SHOULD'VE MADE SURE I STAYED DOWN!

AND I'VE BEEN DEAD BEFORE.

IT ONLY SLOWED ME DOWN.

DAD, I THINK THAT'S ENOUGH FOR TODAY. WHY DON'T WE--

WHAT'S GOING ON IN MY CITY?

WE TOLD HIM.

MY FATHER IS NOT A PATIENT MAN, BUT HE LISTENED WITHOUT INTERRUPTION, WITHOUT DEBATE, UNTIL WE FINISHED.

HE TOOK IT BETTER THAN I THOUGHT HE WOULD.

AT LEAST IT WOULD APPEAR THAT WAY.

IT TOOK A GREAT DEAL OF EFFORT TO BEGIN THIS NEW MISSION OF MY FATHER'S.

HE WANTED TEACHERS. AND RARE ONES.

ONES WHO WERE NOT ONLY GRAND MASTERS IN THE ART OF PHYSICAL COMBAT--

--BUT ALSO POSSESSED THE DESIRE TO INSTRUCT OTHERS IN THE USE OF THESE SKILLS.

AND LASTLY, THEY HAD TO BE WILLING TO JOIN US AT OUR PRESENT LOCATION.

BUT AT THE END OF THE DAY, ALL IT TOOK WAS MONEY. AND THAT, WE CERTAINLY HAD PLENTY OF.

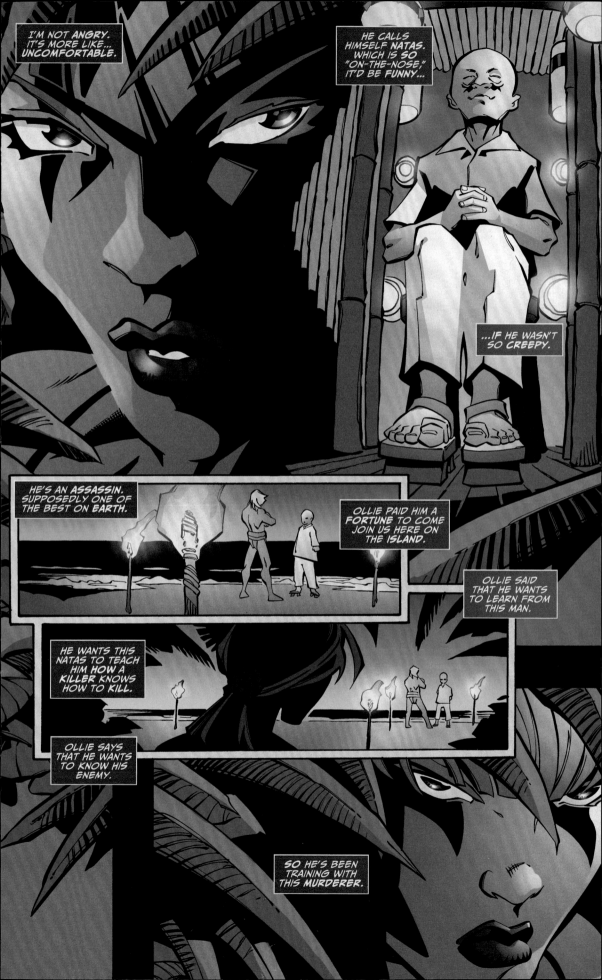

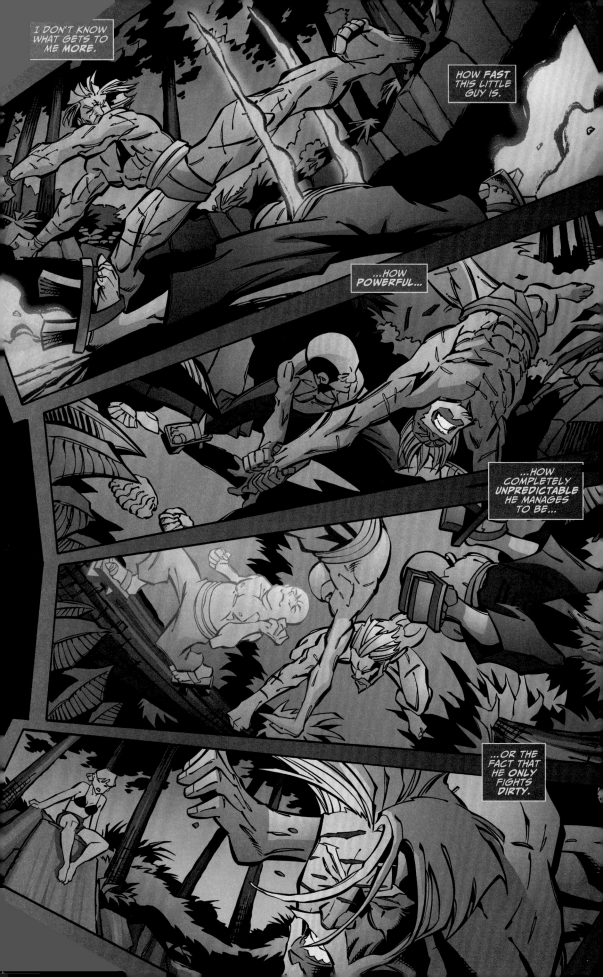

IT WENT ON FOR WEEKS.

THEY WOULD FIGHT. OLLIE WOULD GET HURT.

THEY'D TALK PRIVATELY WHILE OLLIE WAS HEALING UP. OLLIE WOULD CALL IT THEIR "POST GAME" REVIEWS.

LOOKED MORE TO ME LIKE NATAS WAS RUBBING IT IN.

THEN, SOMETHING STARTED TO HAPPEN.

HE WAS BEGINNING TO ANTICIPATE. TO HIT BEFORE GETTING HIT.

OLLIE WAS GETTING BETTER.

AND HE STARTED TO **TAG** THE OLD MAN.

WITH **ALL** THE OTHER TEACHERS WE HAVE ON THIS ISLAND, WHENEVER ME, OR CONNOR AND OLLIE, STARTED TO **LEARN** SOMETHING--

--TO ACTUALLY GET THE **BETTER** OF THEM...WHEN WE STARTED TO **WIN**...

THEY WOULD BE **PROUD.**

THEIR EFFORTS WERE REWARDED. THEIR **STUDENT** HAD GRADUATED TO A HIGHER READING GROUP.

NOT THIS GUY.

OLLIE GOT BETTER. AND IT JUST MADE NATAS MAD.

REALLY MAD.

Y'KNOW THOSE *PINK PANTHER* MOVIES WHERE INSPECTOR *CLOUSEAU'S* ASSISTANT *KATO* ATTACKS HIS BOSS *EVERY* TIME HE COMES HOME?

AND THE ATTACKS BEGAN.

AND THEN THE SPARRING ENDED.

IT WAS A LITTLE LIKE THAT, BUT, Y'KNOW... NOT NEARLY AS FUNNY.

HEY, TUCKMAN. WHAT'S UP?

SOMETHING'S HAPPENED IN STAR CITY.

"THERE'S SOMETHING I NEED TO TELL OLLIE."

A WALL? THEY BUILT A WALL?!

IT'S NOT AS BAD AS THAT.

NO, BUT IT'S A START!

GOD ALMIGHTY, YOU KNOW IF THE EXPLOSIONS HIT DOWNTOWN OR OVER NEAR ADAMS HEIGHTS THEY'D NEVER...

THEY TURNED A QUARTER OF THE CITY INTO A GHETTO?!

INTO A DAMNED CONCENTRATION CAMP?!

SONS OF BITCHES...

A WALL.

FIVE WEEKS AND A STOCK MARKET BOONDOGGLE LATER...

I FIND IT *INTERESTING...VERY* INTERESTING...

THAT YOU CHOSE TO TARGET CORPORATIONS WITH *DEFENSE* CONTRACTS.

HERE YOU ARE ON A *BILLION DOLLAR GRIFT*, TAKING DOWN COMPANIES AND *PROFITING* FROM THEIR DEMISE...

...BUT YOU *STILL* TRY TO MAKE IT AN ACT OF *GOODNESS*.

YOU STILL THINK OF YOURSELF AS A *HERO*.

I NEED MONEY. THEY EARN IT THROUGH *BLOOD*, AND I TOOK IT AWAY FROM THEM.

THESE ARE ASSASSINS.

ENGAGED AND SENT BY A MASTER ASSASSIN. A MAN CALLED NATAS.

NATAS WAS HIRED AND CAME TO BE ON THIS ISLAND TO INSTRUCT OLIVER QUEEN IN THE ART OF MURDER.

THERE ARE MANY TEACHERS ON THIS ISLAND. BUT NATAS IS DIFFERENT.

HE IS LIKE THESE MEN.

HE KILLS PEOPLE FOR MONEY.

AND THEY HAVE BEEN EMPLOYED BY NATAS AND GIVEN ONLY ONE INSTRUCTION.

IT STARTED FOR ME ON AN ISLAND. AN ISLAND JUST LIKE THIS.

THE POOR LITTLE MILLIONAIRE BOY KING WASHED ASHORE FROM A SUNKEN YACHT.

IT WASN'T BRAVERY THAT BEGAN IT ALL. IT WAS HUNGER.

I HAD TO EAT. I HAD TO HUNT.

IT WASN'T BRAVERY.

FATE AND CHILDHOOD IDOLATRY SHOWED ME THE WAY.

I FOUND A DEAD BOAR. I FASHIONED A BOW FROM A TENDON IN ITS LEG AND A THICK REED OF BAMBOO.

THEN I SHOT ARROWS. I SHOT ARROWS SO I COULD EAT. THE MORE I SHOT, THE MORE I ATE.

I GOT BETTER BECAUSE I HAD TO. IT WASN'T BRAVERY.

THEN MEN CAME TO THE ISLAND. THEY WERE RUNNING *DRUGS*. AND TO BE HONEST... THEY FRIGHTENED ME.

SO, FOR WHAT WOULD BE THE FIRST TIME, I *STOPPED* MEN FROM DOING WRONG.

ME AND THE BOW I MADE.

I WASN'T *TRYING* TO BE A HERO. I WAS AFRAID THEY'D FIND ME. I STRUCK FIRST.

NOT LONG AFTER THAT, I WENT HOME. THE *BOW* CAME WITH ME.

THE BOW AND THIS GNAWING IN MY GUT.

SOMETHING HAPPENED ON THAT ISLAND. SOMETHING I CAN STILL NEVER EXPLAIN.

I CAME THERE AS SOMEONE WHO FELT ENTITLED TO EVERYTHING HE HAD.

BUT THERE, I WAS LEFT WITH NOTHING.

I HAD TO LEARN TO FIGHT FOR MYSELF.

AND WHEN MY WORLD WAS RETURNED TO ME AND I NO LONGER HAD TO FIGHT TO HELP MYSELF...

...I WANTED TO FIGHT TO HELP OTHERS.

IT WASN'T BRAVERY. IT WAS JUST WHO I'D BECOME.

AND BE BORN AGAIN.

BUT *THIS* WILL REACH YOU BEFORE THAT *BLADE* CAN COME DOWN.

YOU WON'T KILL ME. THE *CONTRACTOR* SAID YOU WOULD *NEVER* KILL ANY OF US.

I DON'T *HAVE* TO. I CAN JUST *HURT* YOU.

AND I'LL *HEAL*. AND I'LL COME BACK AFTER YOU.

I'VE TAKEN THIS JOB. MY PROMISE IS MY *OATH*. IF MY WORK IS *UNFINISHED*, MY NAME IS *SULLIED*.

IT'S THE SAME FOR *ALL* OF US HERE.

WE *HAVE* TO SEE YOU DIE.

THEN WE'LL HAVE TO MAKE IT *VERY* HARD FOR YOU.

"...I JUST **LOCK** THEM UP."

YOU WANT TO **STAY** ON THE ISLAND?

I'M NOT SURE THAT I'M **DONE** HERE. I THINK IT'S BEST IF I STAY ON WITH THE TEACHERS.

YOU'RE **NOT** TELLING ME THE TRUTH.

NO. I'M NOT. I'M JUST TRYING TO MAKE IT **EASY** FOR YOU.

YOU DON'T WANT ME GOING BACK. NOT **YET** AT LEAST.

YOU'RE GOING BACK TO **STAR CITY** TO RUN FOR **MAYOR.** THAT'S GOING TO GET **UGLY.**

VERY UGLY. I...I CAN HANDLE **EIGHT TONS OF MUD** THROWN IN MY DIRECTION, BUT...

MIA?

SO, AS I WAS TELLING THESE *BUTT MONKEYS* WHO WORKED FOR YOU, Y'KNOW, *BEFORE* YOU MADE THEM *ALL* KINDS OF *DEAD*--

--I DON'T HAVE YOUR GUNS.

I GUESS YOU *KNOW* WHO SCREWED UP YOUR DEAL, RIGHT?

SURE. BUT I WAS HOPING *YOU* COULD HELP ME WITH THAT.

NO.

NICE TALKING WITH YOU.

OH, *C'MON,* BIG BOY. I THINK THAT THIS WAS A *GOOD FAITH* EFFORT ON MY PART.

THESE *BRAIN DONORS* I HIRED WERE GETTING UP IN YOUR GRILLE.

I THINK THAT'S *RUDE,* AND I TAUGHT THEM THE ERROR OF *BAD MANNERS.*

I'M ALSO UNDER FIRE.

HEY, MAN--

YEAH, NOW I'M GETTING NAILED FROM ABOVE AND BELOW!!

CREE.

ASSK!

WELL... HELLO--

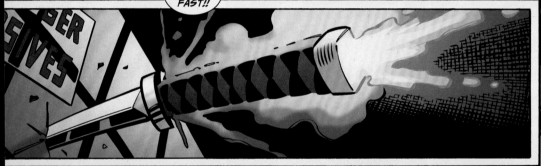

THAT LITTLE SON OF A --!!

CALM DOWN.

I AM CALM... I'M ALSO ENRAGED AND SHOUTING!! HE PLAYED US!

WHAT THE HELL IS THIS ABOUT?! WHY WOULD HE TAKE SPEEDY!?

HE'S MOST LIKELY MAKING A POINT.

WHICH IS WHY IF WE CONTINUE TO SEARCH WE WILL FIND CLUES AS TO WHERE THEY ARE.

WHAT DO YOU MEAN "MAKING A POINT"?

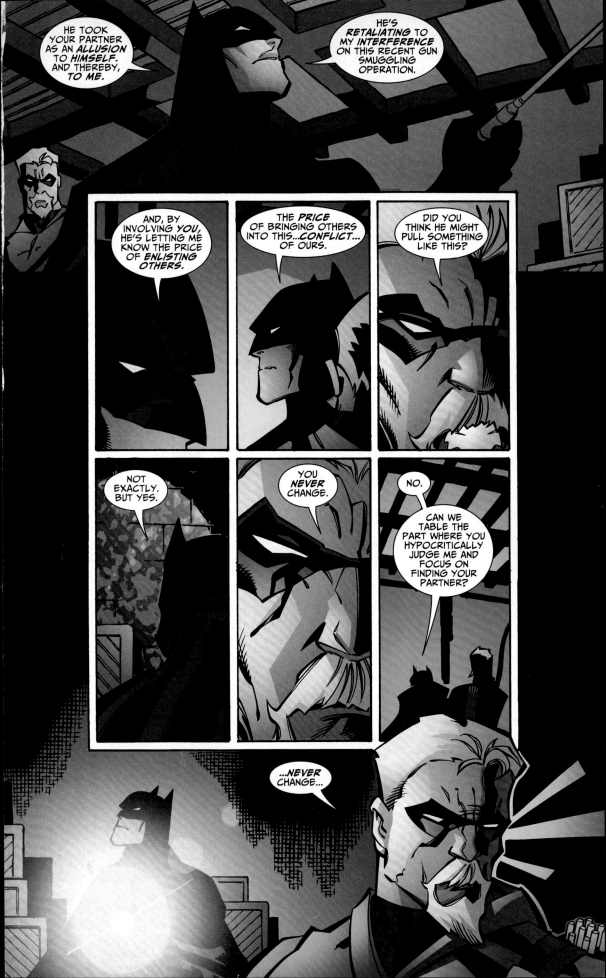

CRACK

BRONNG!

MIA DEARDEN, SEVENTEEN. ABUSED AND FORCED INTO PROSTITUTION BY HER DAD.

A RUNAWAY WHO SOUGHT OUT ONE LOUSY FATHER FIGURE AFTER ANOTHER TO SURVIVE ON THE STREETS.

TURNED TRICKS, SHOT DRUGS AND EVENTUALLY...

MY SURROGATE DAD COMES FROM THE *SAME* DAMNED *PAMPERED* UPBRINGING AS *YOUR* SELF-RIGHTEOUS MENTOR.

LEMME LET YOU IN ON A LITTLE *SECRET...*

I'M LIKE *YOU.* I WAS BORN OUT ON THE *STREETS,* TOO.

I'VE *SEEN* THINGS. I'VE *DONE* THINGS.

I KNOW THAT SOMETIMES WE *HAVE* TO DO THE *BAD* THING JUST TO GET BY.

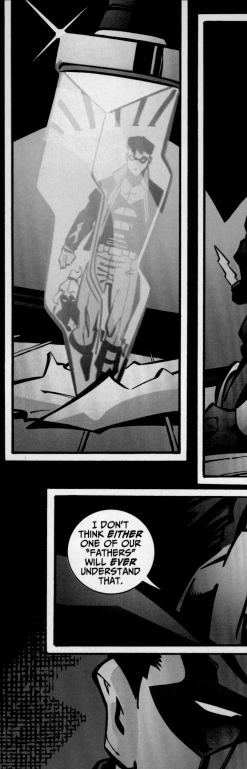

AND I *KNOW* THAT SOMETIMES *VERY* BAD THINGS *HAVE* TO BE DONE TO DO A GREAT *RIGHT.*

I DON'T THINK *EITHER* ONE OF OUR "FATHERS" WILL *EVER* UNDERSTAND THAT.

BUT *YOU* DO.

WHA... WHAT...?

MIA!!!!

HERE.

I MANAGED TO BREAK OUT BEFORE HE BLEW THE PLACE...UNLESS OF COURSE HE LET ME GO...

THE *UPSIDE*, I GUESS, IS THAT I WON'T HAVE TO STUDY FOR TOMORROW'S CHEM EXAM...

ARE YOU OKAY? ARE YOU *HURT?* DID HE HURT YOU?

TALKED?

NO... WE JUST *TALKED.*

YEAH. HE WANTED TO "TEACH ME A LESSON."

SORRY TO HEAR THAT.

OLLIE!! OLLIE, WE'VE-- WE'VE GOT--

GODALMIGHTY--!

WHAT'S WRONG, FRED?

A STORY-- THE PRESS HAS GOT A STORY... THAT'S--

OLLIE... IT'S BAD...

HOW BAD CAN IT BE...

--HAS BEEN VERIFIED THAT THE MONEY HAS COME DIRECTLY FROM MAYOR OLIVER QUEEN'S ACCOUNTS.

AND IN WHAT APPEARS TO BE A CONSCIOUS EFFORT TO HIDE HIS ACTIVITIES--

--THE ACCOUNTS WERE HELD BY SHELL CORPORATIONS AND FICTIONAL INDIVIDUALS.

MAYOR QUEEN

STAR CITY.

A WEARY TRAVELER RETURNS HOME. AND MUCH HAS HAPPENED IN HIS ABSENCE.

A WALL ROSE, BUT VILLAINS FELL.

A HERO ASCENDED TO A PLACE OF PUBLIC OFFICE.

STAR CITY SENTINEL

RECALL ELECTION COUNTDOWN!
1 WEEK TO GO!
NUDOCERDO Favored by small margin

BUT IT SEEMS THAT MAY END.

WELL, YOU *KNOW* THE EXPRESSION. "GUTLESSLY HAUL ASS IN AN S.U.V...."

"...LIVE TO *CRAVENLY* FIGHT ANOTHER DAY."

I'M *NOT* SURE THAT'S HOW IT GOES. AND I THINK IT *RHYMES* A BIT, TOO.

MAYBE. BUT *MY* WAY HAS MORE *STYLE.*

YOU'RE A STYLISH MAN, DAD.

I AM *NOTHING* IF NOT THAT.

WELCOME HOME, CONNOR. I'VE MISSED YOU BOY.

MISSED YOU TOO, DAD.

DAD, I CAN'T *BREATHE.*

TOUGH IT OUT. THIS IS *FATHERLY LOVE* CRUSHING YOUR INNARDS.

OKAY...

FREDERICK TUCKMAN. Advisor to the Mayor.

WHAT DO YOU MEAN?

SHUT *UP*, FRED.

I WILL *NOT*. HE WANTS TO KNOW, SO I'M GONNA *TELL HIM!*

YOUR FATHER COULD *MOW* OVER THESE BASTARDS. AND *ALL* HE WOULD HAVE TO DO IS TELL THE *TRUTH*.

IGNORING THE FACT THAT OLLIE *SHOULD* BE UP FOR A *NOBEL PEACE PRIZE*--

--EVERY ONE OF THESE *SCUMBAGS* THAT IS TRYING TO TAKE HIM DOWN IS *COVERED* IN *MUD!*

NUDOCERDO-- HE'S DIRTY. HE'S BEEN ON THE *TAKE* FOR *YEARS*.

IF YOU THINK BEING *MAYOR* IS GOING TO MAKE HIM *VIRGIN CLEAN* SOMEHOW--

IT'S *NOT* THE POINT.

YOU DIDN'T EVEN AGREE TO A *TELEVISED* DEBATE!!

IT'S NOT THE POINT!!

EVEN IF I WENT FOR THE *JUGULAR*...

...AND DROPPED *EVERY* KIND OF BOMB I COULD--FROM THE PURE POLITICS OF TROTTING OUT STATISTICS...

...TO DIGGING UP *CROOKS* WITH *VIDEOTAPE* OF NUDOCERDO TAKING *BAGFULS* OF MONEY--

--IT'D *STILL* BE A *CLOSE* RACE.

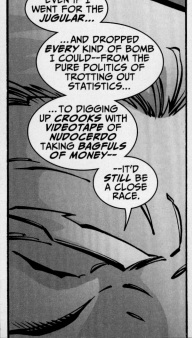

WHAT *IS* THE POINT?

FOR *GOD'S SAKE*, I'VE GOT MY *OWN SON* HERE WHO'S AS MUCH AS TELLING ME THAT I *BANKROLLED* A SUPER TEAM OF *TORTURE-HUNGRY PSYCHOS*--

DAD.

I MIGHT NOT WIN!

SO. I CUT A DEAL.

WHAT DEAL?

THERE'S NO LESS THAN *THIRTY* PROGRAMS THAT WILL KEEP THIS CITY BEING THE *STAR CITY* YOUR FATHER BUILT.

NEEDLE EXCHANGES. FREE CLINICS. DRUG COUNSELING. LOW-INCOME HOUSING.

NUDOCERDO *AGREED* TO LOCK IN THE FUNDING-- *LOCK*--FOR *EVERY* ONE OF OUR PROGRAMS AND *NONE* OF IT CAN BE TOUCHED FOR 15 YEARS.

ALL OLLIE HAS TO DO IS *NOT* FIGHT. *LET THEM WIN.*

AND... THERE'S...

THEY ALSO AGREED TO LEAVE *MIA* ALONE.

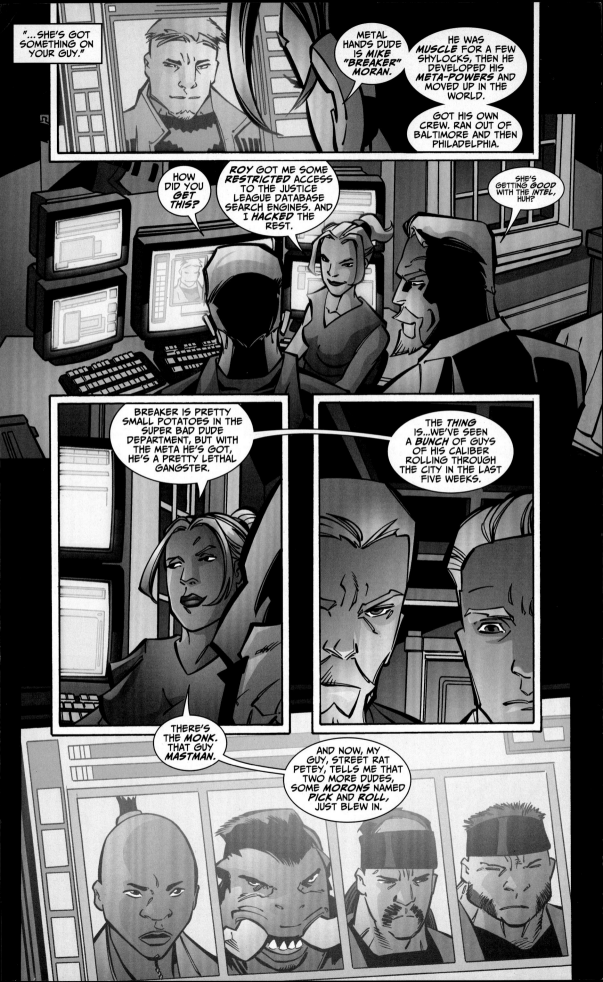

"...SHE'S GOT SOMETHING ON YOUR GUY."

METAL HANDS DUDE IS *MIKE "BREAKER" MORAN.*

HE WAS *MUSCLE* FOR A FEW *SHYLOCKS,* THEN HE DEVELOPED HIS *META-POWERS* AND MOVED UP IN THE WORLD.

GOT HIS OWN CREW. RAN OUT OF BALTIMORE AND THEN PHILADELPHIA.

HOW DID YOU *GET* THIS?

ROY GOT ME SOME *RESTRICTED* ACCESS TO THE JUSTICE LEAGUE DATABASE SEARCH ENGINES. AND I *HACKED* THE REST.

SHE'S GETTING *GOOD* WITH THE *INTEL,* HUH?

BREAKER IS PRETTY SMALL POTATOES IN THE SUPER BAD DUDE DEPARTMENT, BUT WITH THE META HE'S GOT, HE'S A PRETTY LETHAL GANGSTER.

THE *THING* IS...WE'VE SEEN A *BUNCH* OF GUYS OF HIS CALIBER ROLLING THROUGH THE CITY IN THE LAST FIVE WEEKS.

THERE'S THE *MONK.* THAT GUY *MASTMAN.*

AND NOW, MY GUY, STREET RAT PETEY, TELLS ME THAT TWO MORE DUDES, SOME *MORONS* NAMED *PICK* AND *ROLL,* JUST BLEW IN.

WHAT *ELSE* DOES PETEY SAY?

ANYTHING I ASK. PETEY'S GOT A BIT OF AN ITCH FOR ME.

MIA...

HE GOT AN *ADDRESS* FOR WHAT HE THINKS IS A BIG *MEET* TONIGHT.

THESE *OUT-OF-TOWNERS,* AND SOME *LOCALS...* AND...

HE HEARS THAT A *BIGGER GUN* IS ROLLING IN.

HE SAYS THE WORD IS *SOMEONE* IS PUTTING TOGETHER A *NEW CREW,* AND...

BUT AS *LONG* AS Y'ALL CAN FOLLOW ORDERS, I THINK WE CAN GET THIS SHIP TURNED AROUND.

SO, WHAT ABOUT ALL THE TALK ABOUT YOU BEING THE *TOP COP* ON THIS SIDE OF *THE WALL?*

YOU FOUND YOUR *"INNER BADASS"* AGAIN?

I *DID* WHAT I DID. I LOOKED AFTER MY OWN. MY OWN *PEOPLE.* MY OWN *CITY.* MY OWN *BUSINESS.*

I WAS *WAITING* FOR YOU.

OLLIE...

I *WASN'T* GOING TO COME *AFTER* YOU.

I WASN'T GOING TO *PURSUE* YOU ANYMORE.

OH, OLLIE.

I *WANTED* TO BE...I WANTED TO BE A *BETTER* MAN...FOR YOU.

AND I WAS... *PRAYING*...YOU'D SEE IT. SEE WHAT I'VE *DONE*.

TO SEE, MAYBE... *WHO* I'VE BECOME.

I *WANTED* YOU TO COME *BACK* TO ME.

AND HERE I AM.

BLAM!

SOOK

WHERE *ARE* THEY?

UH OH... SOMEBODY'S BEEN, UM, TOUCHING MY CAMERA...

DAMN IT.

G.A...?

MY, *FOUR OF* YOU--

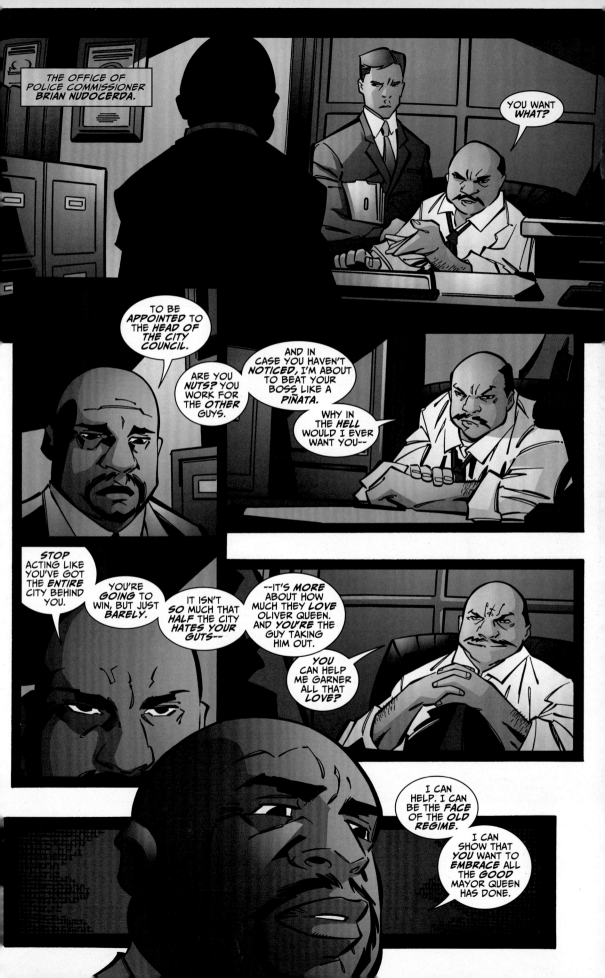

"...HE CAN HANDLE *SHARP* OBJECTS."

I SWEAR, WILSON, IF I DIDN'T KNOW BETTER--

I'D SAY YOU'RE STARTING TO SWEAT!!

CRACK!

I'D AGREE.

NO, *OLIVER.* JUST *DUCKING* THE PUNCHES. ONE OF US WILL TIRE OUT *EVENTUALLY.*

AND IT *WON'T* BE ME.

MAYBE.

CRACK! CRACK!

I MUST ADMIT THAT *BOTH* OF YOU ARE *MUCH* BETTER THAN OUR *LAST* ENCOUNTERS!

IT IS NOT JUST THE *SKILL SETS* YOU NOW EMPLOY, BUT I SENSE A *GREATER* PHYSICAL PROWESS.

AN INNER *STRENGTH.*

A DISPLAY OF *INNER BALANCE.*

I WOULD *NOT* BE SURPRISED TO LEARN THAT YOU STUDIED UNDER SOME OF *MY* FORMER INSTRUCTORS.

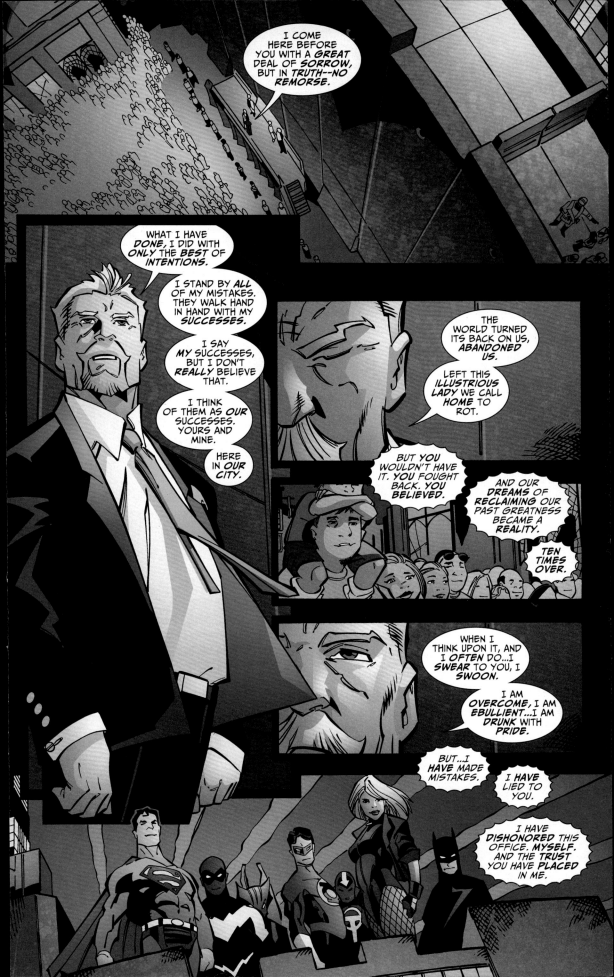

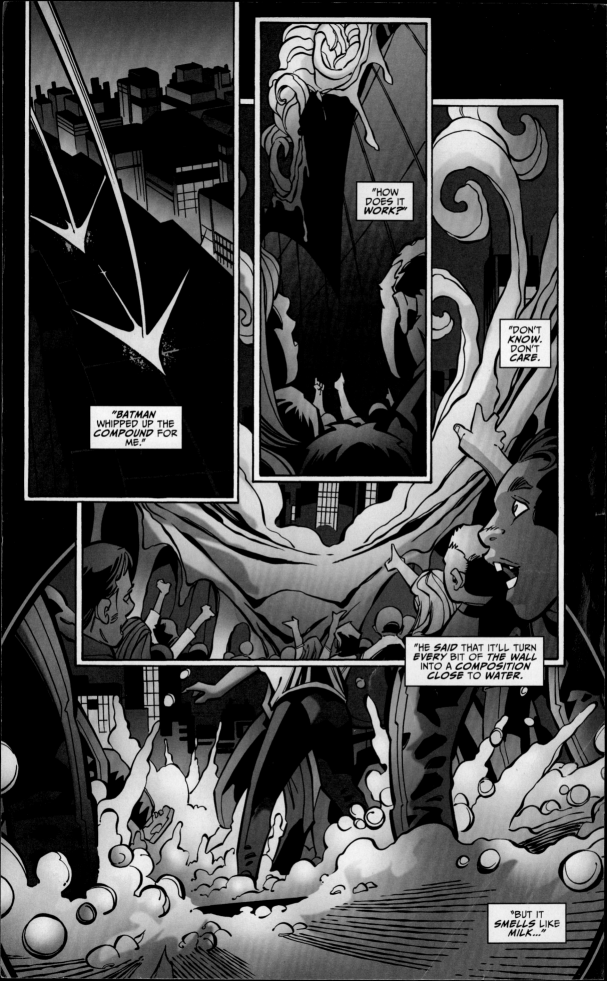